SEE WHAT HAPPENS NEXT ON PAGE 126

£2·25

FUSS POT

TUT! TUT! WHO'S MOVED MY BIKE? I DON'T LIKE IT BEING LEFT IN THE SUN. THE SADDLE GETS HOT! FUSS! FUSS!

AND I'M VERY FUSSY ABOUT THE SHINY NEW PAINT. IT WILL GO ALL DULL IN THE SUN. FUSS! FUSS!

I MUST BE CAREFUL NOT TO GET OIL FROM THE CHAIN ON MY DRESS. I'M VERY FUSSY ABOUT MY APPEARANCE!

FUSS! FUSS! ONE OF OUR CAT'S HAIRS ON MY BLAZER! HOW UNTIDY!

HEY, TIDDLES! YOU'RE IN MY CHAIR! YOU KNOW I HATE ANYBODY SITTING IN MY CHAIR! FUSS! FUSS!

SIGH! SHE DOES GO ON!

5

The HAUNTED WOOD

SON of SIR

Beat your Neighbour

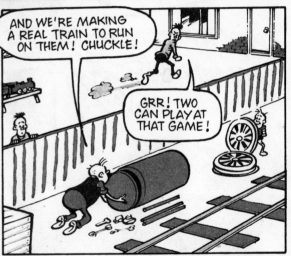

Little Devil

YOU CAN LOOK AFTER THE SPECIAL EFFECTS, JIMMY!

TONIGHT TREASURE ISLAND

WOW! WHAT A PERFECT CHANCE FOR A BIT OF TEMPTING!

HEY! WHY NOT PULL THAT LEVER FOR A BIT OF FUN, KID?

COO! YOU BET, LITTLE DEVIL..!

TEE, HEE! HE MUST BE LOOKING FOR BURIED TREASURE!

YEEARRGH!

DON'T WORRY, LAD! HE WON'T SPOT YOU UP IN THE AIR!

COO! OKAY, LITTLE DEVIL..!

IT WAS JIMMY WHO OPENED THE TRAP DOOR, MISTER!

GRR! WHERE IS HE..?

ARRGH!

WAHAY! THAT KID'S IN EVEN MORE TROUBLE, THANKS TO ME!

THE SUPER SEVEN

THE SUPER SEVEN ARE HERE! WHAT'S WRONG, MATE?

MY BUDGIE'S FLOWN AWAY! I CAN'T SEE HIM ANYWHERE! FIND HIM FOR ME!

EASY! WHISTLER WILL SEND OUT HIS FAMOUS BUDGIE RE-CALL WHISTLE... YOUR BUDGIE WILL HEAR IT WHEREVER HE IS!

PHEEP!

WHO WOKE ME UP?

PHEEEEP!

ME BUDGIE WAS SLEEPING IN THE PILLAR BOX!

HE'S SETTLED UP ON THAT TREE! NEVER MIND, WINDY WILL EASILY FLOAT UP THERE! GIVE HIM THE CAGE!

SQUAWK!

LISTEN! HE'S IN THAT HOLLOW TREE! STINKER, YOU CAN DEAL WITH HIM NOW!

SQUAWK!

ZOOM

YES, ONE BOMB DROPPED IN THERE, AND HE'LL ZOOM OUT OF THAT HOLE IN THE BOTTOM STRAIGHT INTO THE CAGE!

NOT IF I CATCH IT FIRST...! GOT IT... NOW... I'LL GIVE IT BACK TO 'EM!

PHEW! RUN FOR IT! I THINK THAT BUDGIE HAS BEATEN THE SUPER SEVEN!

BOMBS GONE!

PONG!

NOT YET HE HASN'T! LEAVE IT TO ME... DEAD EYE DICK! I'LL FIRE BIRD SEED THROUGH HIS CAGE!

HE'S VERY WEAK! THEY'RE NOT REACHING ME!

FLIP! FLIP!

PONG!

I'LL... HAVE... TO FLY TOWARDS HIM... IF I WANT TO EAT! HE'S GETTING WEAKER!

GOBBLE! GOBBLE!

FLIP! FLIP!

GOT HIM! PHEW!

CLANG!

THANKS, SUPER SEVEN!

I WAS TRICKED!

FUSS POT

OH, THIS COULD BE TROUBLE. FUSS POT WANTS NEW SHOES!

HMM! THESE AREN'T BAD! FETCH ME A BASIN OF WATER!

PARDON?

HUH! *THEY'RE* NO USE! THEY SANK STRAIGHT AWAY! CAN'T BE WATER RESISTANT!

ONE HOUR LATER...

PAH! FUSS-FUSS! I'VE TRIED *EVERY* PAIR IN THE SHOP, AND THIS WAS THE TENTH SHOP I CAME TO! I JUST *CAN'T* FIND WHAT I WANT!

I CAN'T STAND THIS FUSSINESS MUCH LONGER!

JUST A MINUTE! *THOSE* SHOES ARE NEW, AREN'T THEY?

ACTUALLY, YES!

AFTER ALL THAT... SHE BOUGHT *MY* SHOES!

17

MY BRUVVER

DO I HAVE TO TAKE LITTLE'UN TO THE YOUTH CLUB CHRISTMAS PARTY, MUM?

YES, YOU DO, LEN!

AND SOON...

HELLO, LEN! YOU CAN HELP ME GET THINGS READY!

ME WANT TO HELP, TOO!

YOUTH CLUB

WE'RE HOISTING THE BALLOON NET, LITTLE'UN! YOU CAN PUT UP SOME DECORATIONS!

TITTER! ME GOT BETTER USE FOR THESE DRAWING PINS...

DRAWING PINS

HERE'S SOME FOOD FOR THE TABLE..!

EEK! WHASSAT?

BANG!

18

SNIGGER! ME GOT CAKES TO MYSELF!

BAH! WHERE'S THE LITTLE PEST GOT TO?

AHA! HE'S HIDING UNDER THE TABLE...

BUT...

GULP! IT'S JUST LITTLE'UN'S WELLIES!

TITTER! ME TRICK LEN... NOW TO ESCAPE WITH CAKES!

YEEOUCH!

LITTLE'UN HAS TRODDEN ON THE DRAWING PINS HE KNOCKED OVER...!

HO, HO! DON'T WORRY, LITTLE'UN! WE'LL LET YOU DOWN AT THE END OF THE PARTY WITH THE BALLOONS! CHUCKLE!

BAH!

20

23

25

28

The Toffs and the Toughs

MOOSE

SON of SIR

HOUSEY MOUSEY

GRRR! LOOK AT THE **HOLES** IN THAT CHEESE! HOUSEY MOUSEY HAS BEEN AT IT!

YOU'RE NOT GETTING AWAY WITH THAT, PEST!

B...BUT I DIDN'T TOUCH IT!

GASP! PUFF! HE'S ESCAPED INTO HIS HOLE!

PHEW! SAFE AT LAST!

LATER... HMM! THAT OLD **CANNON** HAS GIVEN ME AN IDEA!

ANTIQUES

SO, BACK HOME...

HEH-HEH! I'LL **BLAST** HIM OUT!

BOOOM!

BONEY

39

SAMMY SHRINK

43

THE SUPER SEVEN

LATER, IN THE SOUTH SEAS...

NO, IT WON'T! BET YOU THOSE TWO KIDS ARE KIPPING UNDER A PALM TREE! SO, THUNDERBALL AND ME WILL KNOCK COCONUTS OFF THE TREES... JUST LISTEN FOR THE FIRST "OW" WHEN A COCONUT HITS THEIR HEAD!

PING!

PING!

PING!

CLUNK!

OOG! GLOOP! MUTTER! MUTTER!

BOOTER! HELP THUNDERBALL AND DEAD EYE DICK KNOCK THE COCONUTS DOWN... QUICK!

BONK!

SPLASH!

EASY! ONE GOOD KICK... PLACED RIGHT... AND I'LL KNOCK DOWN EVERY COCONUT!

BOOMPH!

NOT AN "OW" FROM ANY ISLAND! THEY MUST BE WEARING TIN HELMETS!

THEN...

SWELL! GROW! SPROUT!

SCHOOL

GASP! I DON'T BELIEVE IT!

BEANS

THAT'S STRANGE! WHERE DID THIS FUNNY PLANT COME FROM?

OOER...I'D BETTER CLIMB UP TO HIDE BEFORE SIR SPOTS ME!

BUT...

FI...FI...FO...FUM...

G-GASP! IT'S A G-GIANT! I'VE HAD IT...MY JOKING DAYS ARE OVER!

WOW! HE SQUEEZED THE BULB OF MY TRICK FLOWER! CHUCKLE!

ULP!

SQUIRT

SQUEEZE

GRR! WHERE IS THE LITTLE PEST?

RUB RUB

TEE, HEE! I'D BETTER HIDE UNTIL HE CALMS DOWN!

SONNY STORM

SONNY STORM POSSESSED A STRANGE WEATHER-STICK WHICH HAD ONCE BELONGED TO A SIOUX INDIAN MEDICINE-MAN, AND, WITH IT, HE COULD CREATE HIS OWN PRIVATE WEATHER. ONE EVENING, SONNY WAS SITTING AT HOME WITH HIS MUM WATCHING T.V., WHEN THE WEATHER FORECAST CAME ON...

A DEEP DEPRESSION IS MOVING IN FROM THE ATLANTIC, AND HEAVY, CONTINUOUS RAIN WILL REACH SOUTHERN DISTRICTS BY NOON TOMORROW!

OH NO!

WHAT'S THE MATTER, SONNY?

THE CARNIVAL ON THE COMMON OPENS TOMORROW, AND I'M GOING! BUT IF THERE'S HEAVY RAIN, IT'LL SPOIL EVERYTHING!

I AGREE, BUT THERE'S NOTHING YOU CAN DO ABOUT IT!

OH, YES THERE JOLLY WELL IS! IF THAT FORECAST'S RIGHT, I CAN ALTER THINGS WITH MY WEATHER-STICK!

SO NEXT DAY, SONNY WENT TO THE CARNIVAL WELL PREPARED. AND SURE ENOUGH, JUST BEFORE TWELVE...

RAIN! BUCKETS AND BUCKETS OF IT SWEEPING IN FROM THE WEST! RIGHT, HERE GOES!

BY MEDICINE MAN AND MOUNTAIN COL, HALT THE RAIN BEYOND THAT WALL!

NEXT MOMENT, THE WIND DIED... AND THE PELTING STORM STAYED EXACTLY WHERE IT WAS!

GOOD, THAT'S MADE SURE OF A NICE, DRY DAY ON THE COMMON, AT LEAST! NOW TO HAVE SOME FUN WITH MY PALS!

A TURN ON THE DODGEM CARS CAME FIRST...

SMASHIN', EH, SONNY? THE ONLY THREAT IS THE WEATHER - IT LOOKS PRETTY BLACK OUT THERE

PRRANG!

DON'T WORRY, TOMMY! I RECKON IT'S GOING TO STAY LIKE THIS ALL DAY!

BUT TWO HOURS LATER, WHIRLING HIGH ON THE CHAIR-O-PLANES, SONNY NOTICED SOMETHING TERRIBLE!

CR·R·EAK!

OH, GOOD GRIEF! IT'S RAINED FOR SO LONG AND SO HARD IN ONE PLACE, THAT THE WATER'S BUILT UP BEHIND THE WALL! ONE PART IS WEAKENING ALREADY!

SURE ENOUGH, WITHIN SECONDS...

C-CRIKEY, THE WHOLE CARNIVAL WILL BE FLOODED OUT UNLESS I DO SOMETHING FAST!

KER·R·R·ASH!

WAAA! B-BY MEDICINE MAN AND BISON BONES, SEND ME A STORM OF HUGE HAIL-STONES!

SURRROOOSH!

A FIERCE WHISTLING FILLED THE AIR—AND THEN...

G-GREAT, JUST WHAT I WANTED—AN EFFECT LIKE A CONCENTRATED BOMBING ATTACK!

WHEEE

BOOM!

KERWUMPFF!

KR·R·UMP!

FTOOM!

MY "AIR-RAID" HAS FORMED A HUGE CRATER... AND THE WATER'S FLOWING HARMLESSLY INTO IT! THE CARNIVAL'S SAVED!

BLAAM!

WUMMPH!

HEY, WHAT'S GOING ON OVER HERE? WHAT HAPPENED?

THERE WAS—UM—A BUILD-UP OF RAINWATER ON THE HILL—AND THEN A CRATER APPEARED IN THE GROUND! IT WOULD MAKE A NICE BOATING LAKE, DON'T YOU THINK?

BY JOVE, THAT'S A GREAT IDEA!

GOOD, EVERYBODY'S HAPPY! NOW I'D BETTER "RELEASE" THAT RAINSTORM! THE WEATHER FORECASTERS WOULD BE FURIOUS IF THEY KNEW WHAT I'D DONE TO THEIR DEEP DEPRESSION! HEE, HEE!

Little Devil

BEAT YOUR NEIGHBOUR

SON of SIR

SIR WAS TAKING A HANDICRAFTS LESSON...

TODAY, BOYS, I'M GOING TO LET YOU WORK WITH CLAY!

COR! THAT SOUNDS LIKE FUN!

YOU CAN MAKE CLAY *HEADS* OF MY SON — I'M SURE HE'LL BE AN INSPIRATION TO YOU ALL! *H'MM!*

BOOO!

I'LL JUST SIT HERE AND MODEL FOR YOU! *TEE, HEE!*

HUH! THIS'LL TEACH YOU TO BE SO *BIG* HEADED!

HA, HA! SON'S A MODEL TARGET!

GLOOOOP!

SPLUDGE!

AND THIS BIG LUMP OF CLAY SHOULD FIX SIR! *HEE, HEE!*

HERE HE COMES, LADS ...*FIRE!*

HOWZAT!

THWACK!

EEEEEK! HE WAS READY FOR US!

62

WITH THE TOUGHS AS FLAT AS THIS, THEY'LL BLOW AWAY LIKE LEAVES IN THE WIND!

NEXT MOMENT...

POWER ON, AND OFF THEY GO! SO LONG, TOUGHS!

WHOOSH!

BUT THE WIND CHANGED AND...

WITH THE TOUGHS GONE WE CAN COUNT OUR MONEY IN PEACE!

WOW! THE WIND'S BLOWN US RIGHT BACK INTO TOFF TOWERS!

SINCE WE'RE COMING TO BLOWS WITH THE TOFFS, THEIR FAN WILL HELP US GAIN REVENGE!

POWER ON... AND HERE COMES ALL THE TOFFS' LOVELY PAPER MONEY! HEH, HEH!

HO, HO! THE TOFFS ARE WISHING THEY'D STUCK TO COINS NOW, INSTEAD OF THIS PAPER STUFF!

BAH! THOSE TATTY TOUGHS ARE GETTING A SHARE OF OUR POCKET-MONEY, AFTER ALL!

KNOCKOUT

PUZZLE SECTION!

ALL ANSWERS PAGE 80

DISC JUMBLE PUZZLE!

OUR D.J. SEEMS TO HAVE HIS LABELS IN A MESS! CAN YOU UNSCRAMBLE THE LETTERS ON THEM TO FIND THE NAME OF THE WELL KNOWN GROUP ON EACH DISC?

CAN YOU FIND 8 OBJECTS IN THE PICTURE BELOW THAT BEGIN WITH THE LETTERS K-N-O-C-K-O-U-T?

GRAND JUMBLE SALE TODAY

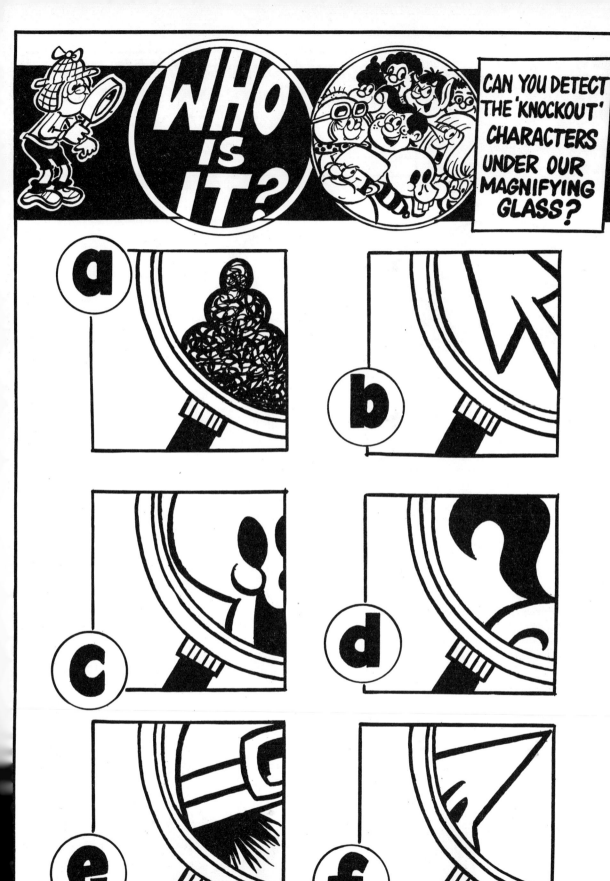

PLACE THE FACE!

Can you say which is the correct face to fit in each of the drawings shown below?

 **A**
 **B**
 **C**
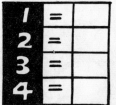 **D**

1	=		
2	=		
3	=		
4	=		

1

2

WET PAINT

3

PAINT

4

ALL MY OWN WORK

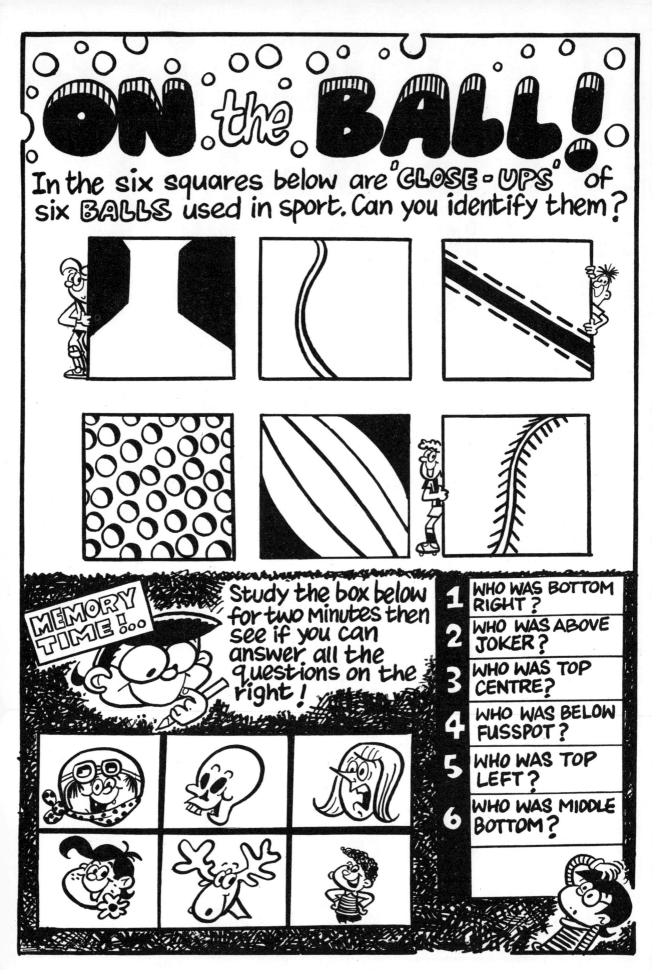

ON the BALL!

In the six squares below are 'CLOSE-UPS' of six BALLS used in sport. Can you identify them?

MEMORY TIME!...

Study the box below for two minutes then see if you can answer all the questions on the right!

1. WHO WAS BOTTOM RIGHT?
2. WHO WAS ABOVE JOKER?
3. WHO WAS TOP CENTRE?
4. WHO WAS BELOW FUSSPOT?
5. WHO WAS TOP LEFT?
6. WHO WAS MIDDLE BOTTOM?

WHO CAN IT BE ????

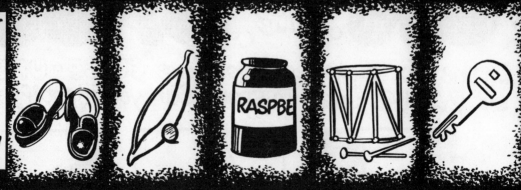

TAKE THE LAST LETTER FROM EACH OBJECT SHOWN TO DISCOVER THE NAME OF A WELL KNOWN **KNOCKOUT!** FUN FRIEND.

SPOTLIGHT!

FIND WHICH SWITCH WILL SWITCH OFF WHICH LIGHT!

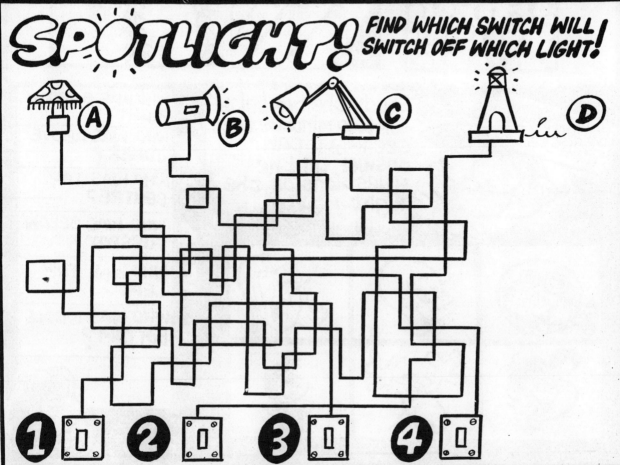

Keen on Sport?

Maybe you are! But not as keen as 'FANATIC FRED' here! Can you say how many SPORTS Fred is interested in?

Feeling Brainy?

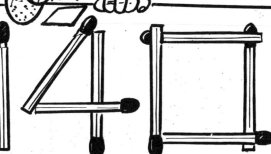

CAN YOU RE-ARRANGE THESE **MATCHES** TO MAKE THE **SUM** of **25**?

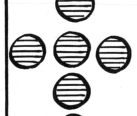

CAN YOU RE-ARRANGE THESE **COINS** THAT FORM A **CROSS**, SO THAT THERE ARE **FOUR** COINS IN THE **HORIZONTAL** LINE, AND **FOUR** IN THE **VERTICAL** LINE!

PUT THE CORRECT SOUND TO THE APPROPRIATE ANIMAL!

FIT THE CLUES TO THE BOX!

TO SOLVE THE PUZZLE! DONT GET CAUGHT!

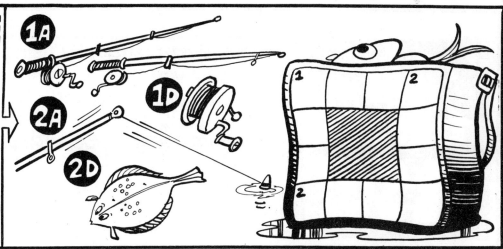

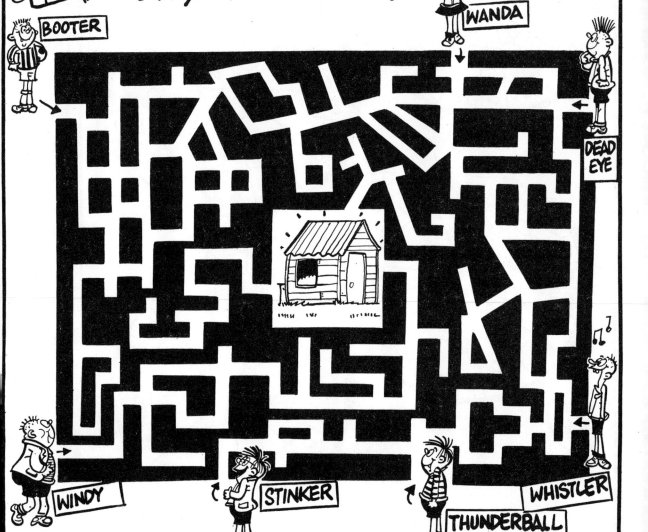

Let's all *meet* at the ganghut! Said **WANDA...**

HOWEVER, only one of the *super seven* reached the **HUT!** Can you find out who!

BOOTER

WANDA

DEAD EYE

WINDY

STINKER

THUNDERBALL

WHISTLER

75

BELOW ALSO!

are four dart-boards. By using the code given on the right you should, by working out the numbers that the darts landed on, and matching these with the code shown, be able to say who threw those darts-also who achieved the highest score!

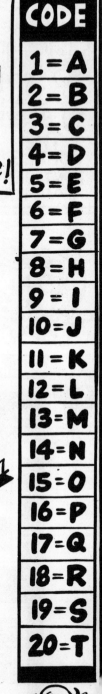

CODE
1 = A
2 = B
3 = C
4 = D
5 = E
6 = F
7 = G
8 = H
9 = I
10 = J
11 = K
12 = L
13 = M
14 = N
15 = O
16 = P
17 = Q
18 = R
19 = S
20 = T

THE CHRISTMAS TOY SEARCH!

Christmas Day is over, and the children have mixed up all their presents! Can you find them in the jumble? Look carefully at the grid for the toys. The words read forward, backwards, up and down, and diagonally. We have found two as an example for you! Merry Christmas! Good hunting!

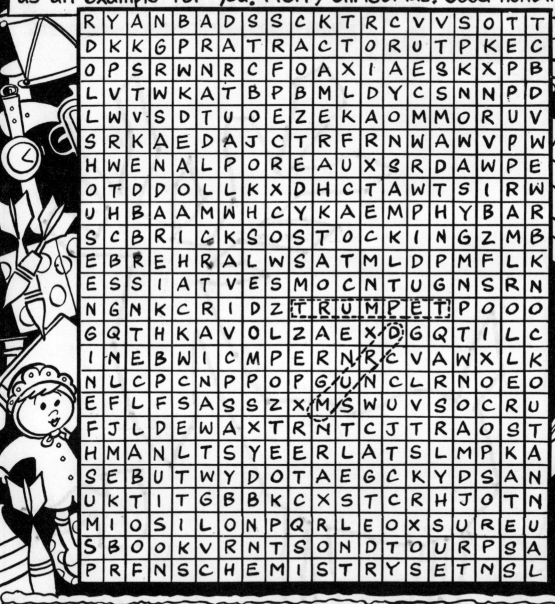

R	Y	A	N	B	A	D	S	S	C	K	T	R	C	V	V	S	O	T	T
D	K	K	G	P	R	A	T	R	A	C	T	O	R	U	T	P	K	E	C
O	P	S	R	W	N	R	C	F	O	A	X	I	A	E	S	K	X	P	B
L	V	T	W	K	A	T	B	P	B	M	L	D	Y	C	S	N	N	P	D
L	W	V	S	D	T	U	O	E	Z	E	K	A	O	M	M	O	R	U	V
S	R	K	A	E	D	A	J	C	T	R	F	R	N	W	A	W	V	P	W
H	W	E	N	A	L	P	O	R	E	A	U	X	S	R	D	A	W	P	E
O	T	D	D	O	L	L	K	X	D	H	C	T	A	W	T	S	I	R	W
U	H	B	A	A	M	W	H	C	Y	K	A	E	M	P	H	Y	B	A	R
S	C	B	R	I	C	K	S	O	S	T	O	C	K	I	N	G	Z	M	B
E	B	R	E	H	R	A	L	W	S	A	T	M	L	D	P	M	F	L	K
E	S	S	I	A	T	V	E	S	M	O	C	N	T	U	G	N	S	R	N
N	G	N	K	C	R	I	D	Z	T	R	U	M	P	E	T	P	O	O	O
G	Q	T	H	K	A	V	O	L	Z	A	E	X	D	G	Q	T	I	L	C
I	N	E	B	W	I	C	M	P	E	R	N	C	V	A	W	X	L	K
N	L	C	P	C	N	P	P	O	P	G	U	N	C	L	R	N	O	E	O
E	F	L	F	S	A	S	S	Z	X	M	S	W	U	V	S	O	C	R	U
F	J	L	D	E	W	A	X	T	R	N	T	C	J	T	R	A	O	S	T
H	M	A	N	L	T	S	Y	E	E	R	L	A	T	S	L	M	P	K	A
S	E	B	U	T	W	Y	D	O	T	A	E	G	C	K	Y	D	S	A	N
U	K	T	I	T	G	B	B	K	C	X	S	T	C	R	H	J	O	T	N
M	I	O	S	I	L	O	N	P	Q	R	L	E	O	X	S	U	R	E	U
S	B	O	O	K	V	R	N	T	S	O	N	D	T	O	U	R	P	S	A
P	R	F	N	S	C	H	E	M	I	S	T	R	Y	S	E	T	N	S	L

DOLLS HOUSE	TRUMPET	ROLLER SKATES	CALCULATOR	TRAIN
DARTS	POP GUN	ENGINE	MODELS	STOCKING
CAMERA	TEA SET	PRAM	SATCHEL	BIKE
RADIO	CHEMISTRY SET	CRAYONS	PUPPET	SKITTLES
AEROPLANE	BOOK	DOLL	DRUM	TRACTOR
WRIST WATCH	BRICKS	FOOTBALL	NECKLACE	KNOCKOUT ANNUAL

KNOCKOUT! CROSSWORD!

Match the picture clues to fill in the crossword!

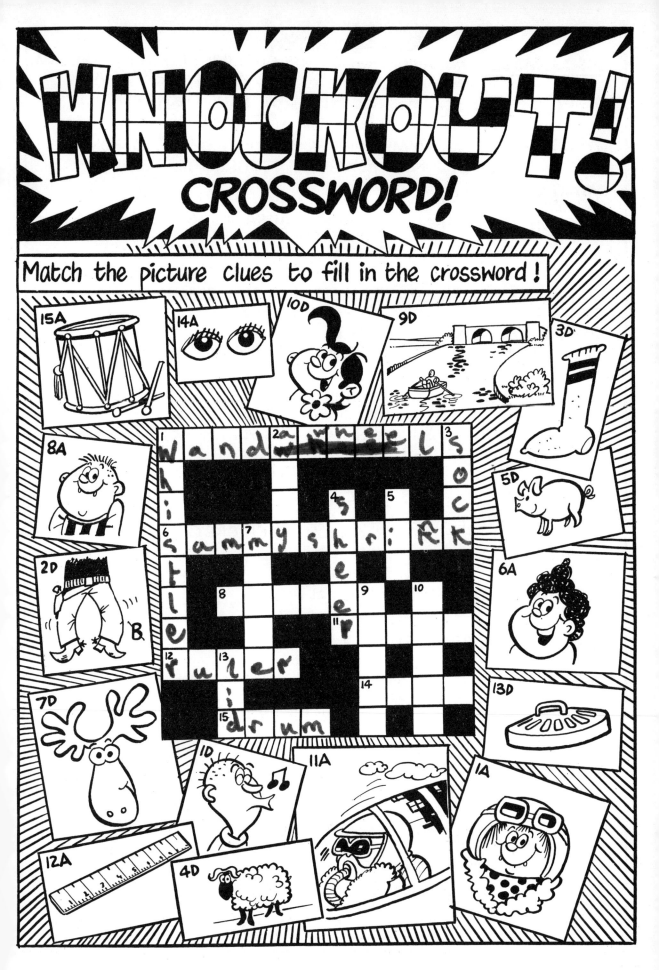

ANSWERS!

DISC JUMBLE:- BAD MANNERS, STATUS QUO, POLICE, BLONDIE, THE JAM, MADNESS, ABBA, THE WHO, WINGS, THE SPECIALS.

K-N-O-C-K-O-U-T:- KETTLE, NET, OWL, CLOCK, KNAPSACK, OAR, UMBRELLA, TRUMPET.

WHO IS IT:- **A.** SAMMY SHRINK. **B.** LITTLE DEVIL. **C.** BONEY. **D.** JOKER. **E.** WANDA. **F.** FUSS POT.

OH DEAR:- 1-E, 2-C, 3-F, 4-D, 5-A, 6-B.

CHARLIE THE CHEF:- GRAPES, SAUSAGES, SWEETS, SPICE, CREAM, MINCE PIES, SPINACH, CHICKEN, NUTS, SOUP, POTATOES, SALAD, DATES, STEAK.

PETE'S POCKET-TRICK:- BUGLE, ONION, NET, ELEPHANT, YACHT. (BONEY)

PLACE THE FACE:- 1-C, 2-B, 3-D, 4-A.

ON THE BALL:- FOOTBALL, TENNIS, CRICKET, GOLF, RUGBY, SOFTBALL.

MEMORY TIME:- **1.** SAMMY SHRINK. **2.** WANDA. **3.** BONEY. **4.** SAMMY SHRINK. **5.** WANDA. **6.** MOOSE.

WHO CAN IT BE?:- SLIPPERS, PEA, JAM, DRUM, KEY, CUPS, FISH, CAR, SKI, GUN, INK. (SAMMY SHRINK)

SPOTLIGHT:- A-3, B-2, C-4, D-1.

KEEN ON SPORT:- RIDING, FENCING, FOOTBALL, BOXING, DARTS, SNOOKER, CRICKET, SKIN-DIVING.

FEELING BRAINY:- 14 + 11 Place on top of coin indicated.

SOUNDS CRAZY:- 1-B, 2-C, 3-F, 4-G, 5-E, 6-I, 7-L, 8-H, 9-D, 10-A, 11-J, 12-K.

BOX:- ACROSS:-**1**, RODS. **2**, LINE. DOWN:-**1**, REEL, **2**, SOLE.

WANDA:- WINDY.

BELOW ALSO:- A-JOKER, B, BOOTER, C, STINKER, D-PETE. (HIGHEST SCORE - STINKER)

SPOT THE DOTS:- MOOSE AND FRENCHY.

TOY SEARCH

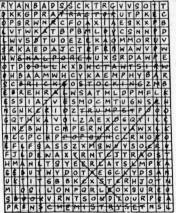

KNOCKOUT CROSSWORD

The HAUNTED WOOD

AND HE DID...

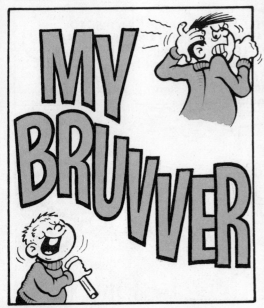

MY BRUVVER

DO I HAVE TO TAKE LITTLE'UN WITH ME ON MY PAPER ROUND, MUM?

YES, YOU DO, LEN!

AND SOON...

NEWSAGENT

OPEN

ME HELP, LEN!

TEE, HEE! ME FILLED MY POCKETS UP WITH **DRIED PEAS** BEFORE ME LEFT HOME...!

YEEOWL!

GRR! THAT'LL TEACH YOU TO WAKE ME UP WITH YOUR **YELLING**!

THUMP!

OUCH!

TERRY BAVE

HOUSEY MOUSEY

Dick Millington

89

Sammy Shrink

HO, HO! THAT LOOKS A BIT TOO BIG FOR YOU TO CARRY, SAMMY!

BAH! NOBODY UNDERSTANDS WHAT IT'S LIKE BEING SO TINY! I'LL BE GLAD TO GET MY NEW ROCKET KIT HOME!

THEN...

SHRIEK! MY TABLECLOTH!

SORRY, MUM IT'S THE ONLY WAY I CAN SQUEEZE THE GLUE TUBE!

GLUE

TAKE IT OUTSIDE!

SIGH! IF ONLY EVERYONE KNEW WHAT IT'S LIKE TO BE SMALL!

BUT SOON...

STILL, SOMETIMES IT CAN BE FUN! NOT EVERYONE CAN PLAY INSIDE THEIR MODEL ROCKETS! CHUCKLE!

H-HEY! IT'S NOT SUPPOSED TO TAKE OFF!

93

THE SUPER SEVEN

ABOUT TIME TOO! THOUGHT YOU WEREN'T GOING TO ANSWER OUR DISTRESS CALL! OUR TWO SOPPY TEACHERS SUDDENLY DECIDED TO TAKE US ON A **LONG** NATURE RAMBLE! WE'LL NEVER GET BACK IN TIME TO SEE THAT SUPER THRILLER ON TELLY. **UNLESS** YOU HELP US!

TO THE WOODS

GATHER ROUND, CHILDREN— SEE THAT WASPS', NEST UP THERE? IT'S FIRMLY FIXED TO THE TREE... SEE! IT WON'T BUDGE.

IT WILL... WITH ONE OF MY THUNDERBALL MARBLES BEHIND IT!

...ER... I'M VERY SORRY, MISS TWITCH! ALLOW ME TO GIVE YOU A BUNCH OF SWEET-SMELLING WILD FLOWERS!

STUNG

...PLUS A FEW OF MY STINK BOMBS!

THANK YOU, MISTER CLINCH. I FORGIVE YOU!

OUCH!

OOF!

JUST YOU WAIT TILL I GET MY HANDS ON YOU!

OOH... OW! I WISH SHE'D SHUT UP... ER LOOK, A RABBIT HOLE. YOU LIKE BUNNIES!

ER... YES... I DO! WONDER IF THERE ARE ANY DEAR LITTLE BUNNIES DOWN THERE!

WHISTLER! TAKE OVER!

PHEEEEP!

AAAGH! AN EXPRESS TRAIN'S COMING OUT OF THE TUNNEL! I MUST GO HOME AND REST! CLASS DISMISSED!

PHEEP!

ER... MISS TWITCH... I HOPE YOU'RE NOT GOING TO BLAME ME FOR THIS!

JUMP ABOARD, KIDS! I'LL GET YOU ALL HOME IN PLENTY OF TIME FOR TELLY!

SONNY STORM

ON HIS WAY TO A FISHING COMPETITION, SONNY FOUND THAT THE LOCAL BULLY, BASHER BRAGG, WAS COMPETING AS WELL...

WOTCHER, STORM! I BET YOU'RE USELESS! I'M GOING TO WIN THIS COMPETITION — BY CATCHING THE BEST AND BIGGEST FISH!

WE'LL SOON SEE ABOUT THAT, BASHER! IT'S SKILL THAT COUNTS AT THIS GAME!

EAGERLY, THE BOYS SET UP THEIR RODS. AND SOON...

A BITE! I'VE GOT A BITE!

SO HAVE I... AND IT FEELS LIKE A WHOPPER!

BUT... HO, HO, HO! CALL THAT A WHOPPER? IT'S NOTHING BUT A MINI-SIZED MINNOW! I'VE LANDED A BIG ROACH!

GAH! DON'T WORRY, THERE'S A LONG TIME TO GO YET!

BUT SONNY WAS THE BETTER FISHERMAN. AND SOON...

EIGHT BEAUTIES SO FAR, BASHER! I TOLD YOU IT WAS SKILL THAT COUNTED!

ONE THING'S SURE — THAT BRAT ISN'T GOING TO WIN IF I CAN HELP IT! SMUG LITTLE SONNY STORM IS GOING TO GET A NASTY SHOCK IN A MINUTE!

STEALTHILY, THE BULLY CREPT THROUGH A SCREEN OF BUSHES. AND...

HEH, HEH! DONE IT! THIS IS GOING TO BE THE FUNNIEST THING EVER!

SNK! SNK!

WITH THE COMPETITION OVER, SONNY PREPARED FOR THE WEIGH-IN. BUT AS HE YANKED HIS KEEP NET OUT...

WAAH... MY FISH HAVE ESCAPED! ROTTEN TOAD, BRAGG — YOU MUST HAVE RIPPED THE NET!

THAT'S RIGHT, CHUMP — WITH THESE! NOW I HAVE A CHANCE OF WINNING AFTER ALL!

SWOOOSH!

THAT'S WHAT HE THINKS! I'LL GET MY OWN BACK BY USING MY WEATHER-STICK!

AND SO...

BY MEDICINE-MAN AND RAINBOW TROUT, I WANT RIGHT HERE, A WATER-SPOUT!

INSTANTLY, A GALE SPRUNG UP, WHIPPING THE WATER INTO A SPIRALLING TOWER...

WHEEOOSSSH!

GREAT, HERE IT COMES. I'D BETTER GET READY!

ON RACED THE WATER-SPOUT... PLUCKING BASHER FROM THE BANK LIKE A GIANT HAND!

HEE, HEE! JUST PERFECT! EVEN THE FISH I CAUGHT EARLIER ARE BEING WHISKED BACK UP OUT OF THE RIVER!

VRUUSSSSH!

YAIEEEEEE!

PIN! PLOP!

FLUMP!

AS SONNY WAVED HIS STICK AGAIN, THE WIND DROPPED, AND...

SPLAADOOSSSH!

GLUG-BLUG-UGG!

OOH-UUH-AAH... W-WHAT HAPPENED?

I'D SAY YOU WERE CAUGHT IN A FREAK STORM, BASHER! BETTER HURRY UP, OR YOU'LL MISS THE WEIGH-IN!

THE RESULT WAS FUNNY, TO SAY THE LEAST!

THE WINNER IS SONNY STORM... WHILE THE BOOBY PRIZE GOES TO B. BRAGG FOR THE LANDING OF ONE MINNOW WEIGHING EXACTLY ONE AND A HALF OUNCES!

HA, HA! POOR OLD BASHER! HE CAN'T FISH FOR TOFFEE!

NO, BUT PERHAPS THAT'S WHAT HE SHOULD FISH FOR! IT WOULD AT LEAST STICK TO HIS HOOK!

BAH!

HO, HO!

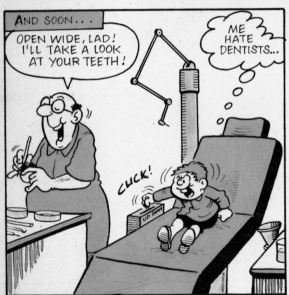

105

SAMMY SHRINK

107

The HAUNTED WOOD

109

The Toffs and the Toughs

111

THE **SUPER SEVEN**

HOUSEY MOUSEY

WARM GLOW!

COR! IT'S LOVELY LIVING IN MR. BINGO'S NICE WARM HOUSE WHEN IT'S FREEZING COLD OUTSIDE!

WOW! A LOVELY PIECE OF CHEESE!

YOW! I C-CAN'T STOP!

SLITHER!

SLIP!

'BYE-EEE!

HAR-HAR! AT LAST I'VE GOT THAT MOUSE OUT OF THE HOUSE!

LATER...

HE MUST BE FROZEN SOLID BY NOW — I'LL GO AND TAKE A LOOK AT MY HANDIWORK!

LOOK AT THAT! A MOUSE LOLLY!

BONEY

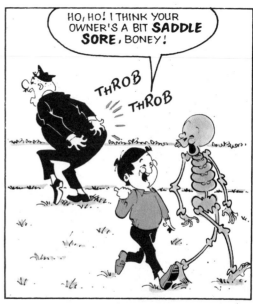

121

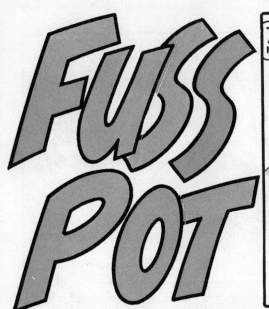